MINDING ME

BOOK ONE

Social, Personal and Health Education

for First-Year Students

Anita Stackpoole

MENTOR
BOOKS

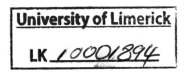
MENTOR BOOKS
43 Furze Road
Sandyford Industrial Estate
Dublin 18
Tel: 01-2952112
Fax: 01-2952114
Website: www.mentorbooks.ie
Email: admin@mentorbooks.ie

Text:	Fiona Chambers
	Anne Jones
	Anita Stackpoole
Edited by:	Deirdre O'Neill
Artwork:	Brian Fitzgerald
	Anita Stackpoole
Design & Layout:	Chris Flynn
Series Editor:	Kate O'Reilly

ISBN: 978-1-84210-429-3

1 3 5 7 9 10 8 6 4 2

Printed in Ireland by
ColourBooks Ltd.

CONTENTS

Foreword

Hi there,

Before we begin, we need to answer some of your questions.

What is this book about?

The hint lies in the title . . . *Minding Me.* Yes, believe it or not, the answer is YOU. This entire book is about you. It is about you as an individual, as a friend, as part of a family and as part of a community.

What can I learn from this book?

Well, first of all you are going to learn about yourself, your values and ideals. You will also have a chance to form opinions on many key life issues. But remember, to get the most out of the book you will need to listen to and respect the opinions of those around you and not be afraid to discuss your own ideas.

How can I use this book?

You will have one class a week of SPHE this year. The teacher will lead you through the lessons. We think you are really going to enjoy this book as you will explore each of the ten modules using a variety of different activities. Sometimes you will be talking and sharing thoughts and ideas. At other times you might be working alone on some personal activities. You will also have a chance to learn more about the modules through research projects.

Why is SPHE so important?

Because YOU are important and SPHE lessons help you to realise just how special you are.

Fiona, Anne and Anita

MODULE 1

Belonging and integrating

This module looks at the challenges of starting something new. Starting in a new school means learning a lot of new information, such as getting to know new people, a new school, new routines and school rules.

Steps to help deal with all of these changes are suggested under the following headings:

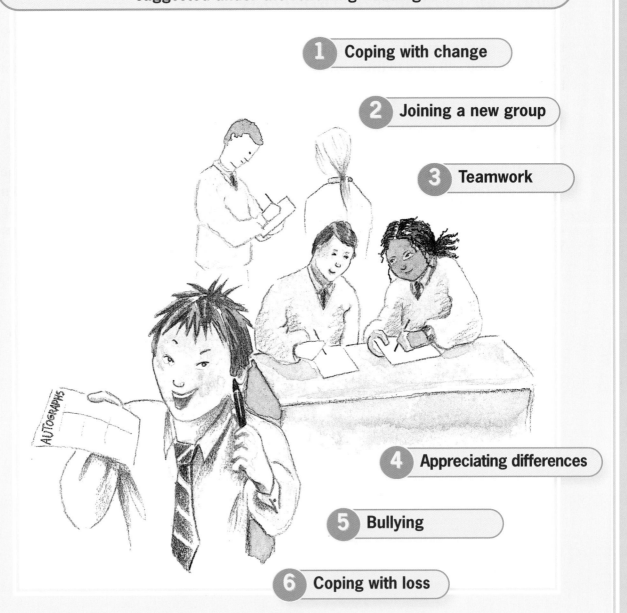

1. Coping with change

2. Joining a new group

3. Teamwork

4. Appreciating differences

5. Bullying

6. Coping with loss

1. Coping with change

New Start, New School

Starting in a new school can be a time of great change for you. You do not know what to expect exactly, but you may have been told how big the school is or how many new teachers you will be meeting. Some of these changes might be exciting for you, and some may seem a bit nerve-racking. The good thing about starting something new as part of a new group is that you and your classmates will be going through this experience together.

1 In your new school, what are the changes you are looking forward to the most and the least?

The things my class is looking forward to the most	The things my class is looking forward to the least

So what's new?

Having moved school, you will notice some differences between your primary school and your secondary school.

2 In the box below, can you list five things that are the same and five things that are different about your new school?

Things that are the same	Things that are different

3 Which changes have been easy to get used to and which changes have been difficult?

_____

_____

_____

Dealing with difficulties

If you do not understand something in class, ask the teacher to explain it to you either during the lesson or at the end of the lesson. You could always ask one of your classmates – this is a good way of getting to know someone. You could also talk to your family about any difficulties you have.

4 Can you think of any other suggestions that could help you deal with difficulties?

_____

_____

What's the story if...?

Your new school will have guidelines on what to do or who to see in certain situations.

5 Who should you speak to in each of the following situations?

If you are late to school _____

If you must leave school early _____

If you lose or find something _____

If you need a locker or have lost a locker key _____

If you have an injury _____

If you are feeling unwell _____

If you have a personal problem _____

If you are being bullied _____

If you see someone being bullied _____

ST. PATRICK'S
Secondary School
Rules and
Guidelines

2. Joining a new group

Fast Friends

In your secondary school, you may notice that there is more than one first year class. For some of your lessons you may be taught as a class group with a class name, while for other subjects you may join a new group. Trying to get to know so many new names and faces can be difficult. Some fun and simple exercises can help you become part of the group.

1 In the first box on the following page write your name and three things you like about yourself or of which you are most proud. On the teacher's signal move to a person you don't know, or the person sitting next to you, and ask them to write, in the next box, their autograph and three things that they like about themselves or of which they are proud. On the teacher's signal move again, and keep moving until you have filled the boxes with names.

Autograph

2 To test your memory, look around the class and try to identify the people who signed your sheet.

3 Did you discover anything new about your classmates? If so, write it in the space below.

_____

_____

3. Teamwork

Working as a team

Another activity that can help you get to know your classmates is to work together as a group. Group work means breaking up the class into groups/teams of about five or six so that each person can share their ideas more easily than by talking to the whole class. Sometimes the purpose of group work is to gather each student's ideas to share with the class.

GROUP ACTIVITY

In this group work exercise, the purpose is for the group to come up with an agreed decision.

Making a new world
It is 2105 and the earth is running out of resources. A new planet has been discovered that is suitable for human life. The World Federation of Governments (WFG) has voted to send humans to live on the new planet. It needs to send four people to prepare the planet for human life. The list of possible people is as follows: scientist, doctor, pregnant woman, builder, plumber, computer technician, horticulturist, artist, engineer, electrician, solicitor, sound technician, police officer, teacher, religious preacher, mechanic.

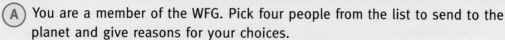

A You are a member of the WFG. Pick four people from the list to send to the planet and give reasons for your choices.

Person 1: _____

Person 2: _____

Person 3: _____

Person 4: _____

B Can you think of any other people who could be added to the list?

_____

Teamwork feedback

Having worked as part of a group, you will now have a better understanding of how teamwork happens. However, sometimes teamwork does not work out for a variety of reasons. Recall your experience of working as a team by answering the following questions:

1 When working as a team, it is always best to start with identifying what went well. What, in your opinion, did your team do well? Can you explain how your team achieved this?

_____

_____

2 What, in your opinion, did your team do poorly? Can you explain how your team did this?

_____

_____

3 Using the information you have gathered, suggest ways to create a 'class charter for working in groups'.

> The whole class can make the class charter. Each group can take an agreed rule, write it out in big writing, decorate it and then attach it to a 'charter poster'. This poster can act as a reminder of how to get the best out of group work activities (see example on page 7).

EVERY PERSON has the right to be ... or needs to be ... SAFE & LOVED

Rights and responsibilities

Every person (parent, student, teacher, etc.) has rights, and these rights are linked to our individual needs.

It is important to remember, however, that with every right comes a responsibility, e.g. I have the right to be safe and I also have the responsibility not to interfere with the safety of others. In other words, my actions should not interfere with the rights of others.

4 List the rights that everyone is entitled to and the responsibilities associated with each right in the table below.

Rights	Responsibilities

Rules

Rules are made to ensure that a person's rights are protected. Can you see how some of these rights are similar to the rules you made up for your class charter for working in groups?

5 Add any new rights to your class charter for working in groups, if you notice they are missing.

Class Charter

The list of ground rules to protect the rights of every person in our group

_____

_____

_____

_____

_____

_____

_____

_____

_____

_____

Signed: _____

_____

Date: _____

4. Appreciating differences

Respecting people

Being different is what makes us interesting. Our world is made up of people from different races with different thoughts, beliefs, religions and cultures. Another word used to describe all this difference is diversity. Respecting our differences is important so that everyone feels valued as an individual.

1 The tree exercise below will demonstrate how diverse your class is. In the space below, draw the different parts of a tree to represent different experiences in your life. Start with the roots and write beside the roots the things you believe in.

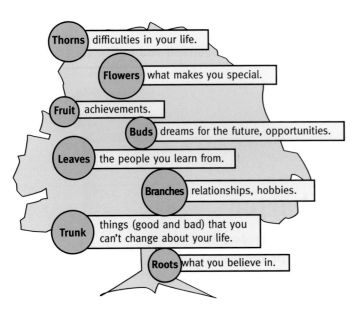

Thorns difficulties in your life.

Flowers what makes you special.

Fruit achievements.

Buds dreams for the future, opportunities.

Leaves the people you learn from.

Branches relationships, hobbies.

Trunk things (good and bad) that you can't change about your life.

Roots what you believe in.

All our tree drawings are different because we are unique. To create a class forest you can trace your tree onto a new sheet and hang it up on the wall beside your fellow classmates' trees. Notice how different each tree looks. Each of our trees represents our personalities and our lives. We are all unique and special.

5. Bullying

1 From what you have learned in primary school, can you recall what you think bullying means?

_____

_____

2 Look at these pictures and name the different types of bullying you see.

_____   _____   _____

3 Can you name some other kinds of bullying?

_____

_____

4 When you think about a person that is being bullied, can you try to imagine what they are feeling? Write down the words and descriptions that come to mind.

_____

_____

5 Why do you think people bully?

_____

_____

6 Why are some people bullied?

_____

_____

7 How might (a) pupils, (b) teachers, (c) schools, and (d) parents prevent bullying?

_____

_____

8 What is the anti-bullying policy in your school?

_____

_____

9 To whom could you talk if you were being bullied?

_____

_____

ACTIVITY

Plan an anti-bullying campaign for your class or school.

(A) Decide upon a slogan that emphasises how your school does not tolerate bullying, such as: 'Stand Up', 'Be a Friend' or 'Respect for All'.

(B) Decide upon a symbol that will signify that you do not support bullying behaviour, for example a shape, a coloured ribbon or a wristband.

(C) Design posters using your slogan and symbol. Hang these posters up around the school to publicise the campaign.

(D) Collect the materials needed to make your symbol. You can distribute these in your school for students and teachers to wear to show how they do not support bullying. Send any money you raise to a charity such as the ISPCC, an organisation that works towards supporting victims of bullying.

> This activity could be linked to a CSPE action project.

6. Coping with loss

The experience of loss is always a difficult one. However, it is our experience of loss that makes us appreciate life and what it has to offer. Loss leads to change and can help us to learn how to cope when someone or something special leaves our lives.

(1) There are many types of loss. Can you add more to the list below?

Family member dying
Health problems
Pet dying
_____
_____
_____
_____

ACTIVITY

Read the letter below and write a reply.

Dear Dora,
I am twelve years old and have just started in first year. I am finding it really hard and really miss my old school. Everything is so different. Everyone is bigger than me. I can't find my way around and keep getting lost. I haven't made any friends yet as there is no one from my old school here. I dread going to school every day.

Amy

Effects of loss

People cope with loss in different ways, but the effects felt are generally the same. Loss affects people emotionally, physically and socially.

Emotional effects of loss A person may:	Physical effects of loss A person may:	Social effects of loss A person may:
◆ Feel depressed or anxious ◆ Seem quiet or withdrawn ◆ Be angry and not know why ◆ Feel lonely ◆ Feel sorry for themselves	◆ Go off their food ◆ Overeat ◆ Get skin rashes or skin complaints ◆ Find it difficult to sleep at night ◆ Find it difficult to get up in the morning	◆ Not want to meet their friends ◆ Not pay attention at school ◆ Become disruptive in class ◆ Feel different from their classmates and friends

When someone suffers a private loss, they can sometimes feel that no one understands what they are going through and they may find it difficult to tell people how they feel. Keeping feelings bottled up inside can make things even harder, so it is important to try and talk to someone. You can help simply by listening to your friends and allowing them to express their feelings.

2 How would you support a friend through this time?

_____

_____

_____

_____

Support strategies

1. You must still take care of yourself when you have suffered a loss. Eating well will help boost your immune system.
2. Talk to people – family, friends, your faith community and other professionals. Talking and listening will give you time to grieve.
3. Express your emotions through art, diary entries or creative writing. Releasing how you feel inside in this way will help you to feel better.
4. Share memories and funny stories. Humour has a great healing power in times of stress.

'Time is a great healer' is a common phrase that rings true. The best way to cope with grief is to allow it time. This gives us the space to adapt so we can move forward with life at a gentle pace.

Helpful websites
www.rainbowsireland.com
www.spunOut.ie
www.ispcc.ie
www.coolschoolbullyfree.ie

MODULE 2

Self-management: A sense of purpose

You have your timetable at this stage, and your new books!
Now it is time to find out how to 'get organised'.

You will need to learn about:

1. Organising yourself

2. Organising your work at home and at school

3. How to get balance in your life

1. Organising yourself

Comparison

Believe it or not, sometimes it is easier to look at how organised other people are before you can look at how organised you are yourself. So this is where we will start. First read how Helen and Liam prepare for their school day, then answer the questions that follow.

The alarm goes off at 8.00 a.m. and Helen jumps out of bed and prepares herself for school. She has to bring her PE gear and her art portfolio, so she makes sure she has everything she needs before having breakfast. She will be in trouble if she forgets these extra things. She is finishing her breakfast as her best friend Louise calls to the door. Both girls head off at 8.30 a.m.

Liam has forgotten to set his alarm clock and doesn't wake up until 8.15 a.m. He is supposed to meet his friend Karen at 8.30 a.m. He jumps out of bed, washes himself, gets dressed and grabs his schoolbag before leaving the house. He realises on the way to school that he has forgotten his football gear for his match and the ingredients he was supposed to bring for his home economics class, but he didn't have time to prepare them this morning.

1. What difficulties could Helen experience in her school today?

_____

_____

2. What difficulties could Liam experience in his school today?

_____

_____

3. If you had to choose, which story describes you best? Why?

_____

_____

Create

Let's try to get Liam more organised…

④ First, look at the list of what Liam needs to do to get ready for school. Write down how much time it might take to get each item ready. Put a number beside each item on the list to show what needs to be done first, second and so on.

	Time Allowed	Sequence
Make sure schoolbag is packed		
Set alarm		
Have a shower		
Buy home economics ingredients		
Eat breakfast		
Wash and dry football gear		
Brush teeth		
Do homework		

	Time Allowed	Sequence
Get breakfast ready		
Lay out uniform		
Prepare school lunch		
Watch film		
Clear away breakfast things		
List home economics ingredients		
Put football gear where it can be found		

2. Organising your work at home and at school

Timetable

	Mon	Tues	Wed	Thurs
9.15	English	Irish	Geography	History
9.50	English	Maths	French	English
10.25	French	History	Art	Geography
11.00	Break	Break	Break	Break

① List some school activities for which you need to be organised:

Activity	Organisation needed

Schoolwork

Being ready for school activities is really only half the battle. It's also very important to sort out how you can keep on top of schoolwork.

Here are some tips for keeping on top of schoolwork. We have left out some key words. Can you fill in the blanks from the list of words below? Report your answers back to the class.

Phone calls; weekend; study; homework; 5-minute;
table; chair; completed; timetable; homework journal; time.

1. Always write your homework in your _____ after each class period.

2. Keep a copy of the _____ at home and on your locker door.

3. Make a _____ plan for each day of the week and follow it.

4. Study at the same _____ every day during the week.

5. Have a comfortable _____ and _____ for doing your homework.

6. Take a _____ break every twenty minutes when doing your homework.

7. Mark completed _____ in your journal.

8. Do not answer _____ from friends until your homework is _____.

9. Select times at the _____ for study.

In summary

To get organised:
- List what needs to be done each day.
- List what you need to do in order of importance.
- Keep on top of schoolwork by following the above tips.
- Make sure that you build in some time for rest and relaxation.

3. How to get balance in your life

Balance

Imagine that your life is a wheel made up of eight segments. The wheel represents the balance in your life. If one segment is significantly larger or smaller than the other segments, this will stop the wheel from turning. Spending too much time watching TV or too little time exercising will create imbalance.

Wheel of Life

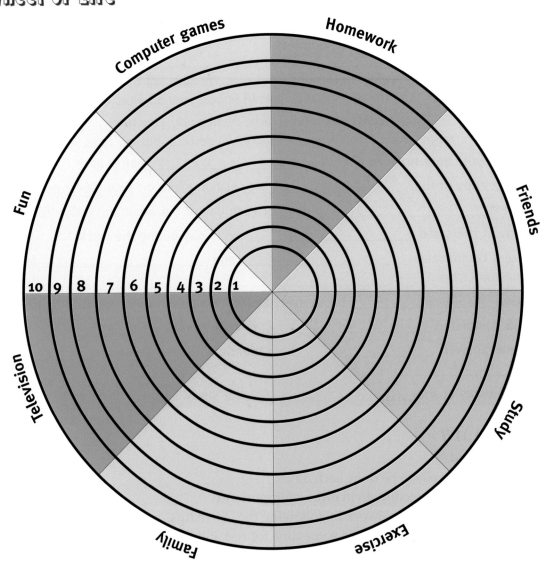

Computer games

Homework

Friends

Fun

10 9 8 7 6 5 4 3 2 1

Study

Television

Exercise

Family

① On the wheel above, work out how many hours per week you give to each segment.

② Can your wheel turn? If not, what can you change in your life to make your wheel turn?

DON'T FORGET THERE ARE PEOPLE AROUND YOU WHO CAN HELP.

In the next section we will explore this idea.

MODULE 3

Communication skills

This module is about communicating with each other.

Communication involves sharing with other people how we think and feel about what is happening in the world around us. It is very important that we express ourselves clearly so that the message we are giving is not confusing. It is equally important to listen to the messages others give us about how they think and feel. We call the skills we use to give and receive messages our communication skills.

In this module you will find out how to improve your own communication skills by:

1. **Expressing yourself**

2. **Learning to listen**

3. **Using different types of communication**

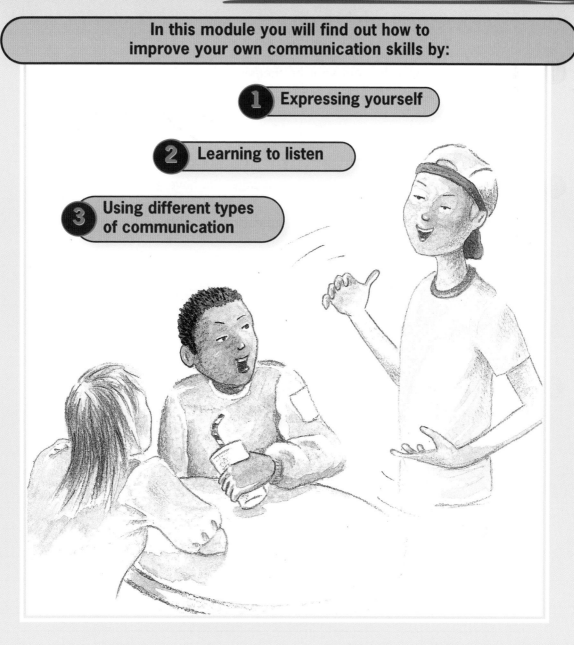

1. Expressing yourself

Good communication skills improve our relationships with the people around us. There are two key communication skills: **body language** and **eye contact.**

Body language

Clenching your jaw, folding your arms, flipping your hair, or even a slight eyelash flutter – these tiny actions can reveal many messages about how we feel. Body language is non-verbal communication or communication without words.

It is a known fact that we notice the non-verbal communication in a speaker more so than his or her words. In fact, a leading sociolinguist (a person who studies how people use language) discovered that:

◆ 7% of any message comes from the words we use.

◆ 38% comes from the voice (tone) we use.

◆ 55% comes from our body language.

1 How do you know what humour your brother/sister/friend is in when you meet up? What clues help you?

_____

_____

2 In pairs, can you list four types of body language? We have given you one example to start you off . . .
Facial expressions, e.g. raised eyebrows, grimacing, tilt of head.

i _____

ii _____

iii _____

iv _____

3 Read your answers back to the class.

In groups of three, describe the body language of each of the following people:

(a) An angry person:

_____

_____

(b) A frightened person:

_____

_____

(c) A bully harassing his/her victim:

_____

_____

(d) An excited person:

_____

_____

(e) A person telling a lie:

_____

_____

Eye contact

◆ Why is making eye contact important when you are talking to someone?

◆ What does it mean when someone is making eye contact with you?

④ Take turns talking to the person beside you without making any eye contact. Share how it made you feel.

2. Learning to listen

Listening

Listening is just as important as making eye contact when conversing. Listening well is called 'active listening' because you are participating in what the other person is telling you.

Some people are very good listeners. Other people, however, act as if they cannot wait to do the talking – they end up interrupting instead of waiting and listening.

> Most of us can sense when a person is listening to us (or not). If we feel that we are not being listened to, then we may stop sharing our thoughts with that particular person.

Homework

⑤ Watch one of your favourite programmes tonight on television. Pick any two characters and listen to them talking to each other for two minutes. Then try to answer the following questions:

(a) Describe what the conversation was about.

_____

_____

_____

(b) How did each character express their feelings during the conversation?

_____

_____

(c) Were the characters listening to each other? How did you know?

_____

_____

(d) How easy or difficult did you find this exercise?

_____

_____

_____

ACTIVITY

In pairs, can you summarise the characteristics of good communication?

_____

_____

_____

It's not all talk . . .

So far, we have spoken about how able-bodied people communicate with each other.

6 (a) Describe a person who might find it difficult to communicate with others.

_____

_____

(b) Which communication skills can they not use?

_____

_____

(c) Suggest ways in which this person could communicate with others.

_____

_____

(d) How might others communicate with this person?

_____

_____

3. Types of communication

Using passive, assertive and aggressive communication

(7) You are queueing at a bus stop for fifteen minutes. Just as the bus arrives, someone jumps ahead of you.

(a) Describe how you feel and what you want to do.

_____

_____

_____

(b) You probably react in one of three ways:
Passively, Aggressively or **Assertively.**
Which way describes how you want to act in this situation?

_____

Communication type	Typical actions	Common expressions
Passive	◆ Often say 'yes' when they mean 'no'. ◆ Will hardly ever voice their true feelings. ◆ Avoid eye contact. Slouch. Unable to receive compliments.	'Sorry, sorry.' 'I don't mind – whatever you like.' 'Err, um.' 'Excuse me.'
Aggressive	◆ May insult or humiliate others, picking on passive people in particular. ◆ Shout, threaten and stare at people to get what they want. ◆ May point their finger, fold their arms and stand upright.	'You had better . . .' 'Yes you will!' 'Idiot.'
Assertive	◆ Speak clearly and calmly without shouting. ◆ Make eye contact. Stand upright with head held high. ◆ Walk confidently. Do not depend on other people's approval.	'I feel . . .' 'Can we discuss . . .?' 'I would like . . .'

671742 X

Be careful!

Assertiveness is not to be confused with getting your own way all of the time. Working and compromising with others is another way of being assertive, while showing self-respect and respect for others.

8 You are in a café and have just ordered lasagne and salad. When the food arrives, the lasagne is cold and there is a slug in the salad.

Working in pairs, decide how the following people would react:

(a) A passive person

_____

_____

(b) An aggressive person

_____

_____

(c) An assertive person

_____

_____

Be careful!

People do not become assertive overnight. Becoming assertive takes practice. So, every time you need to share your feelings about something important, try being assertive . . . it really works!!

ACTIVITY

This activity will show you how to put your communication skills into practice!

(Look again at your class charter for teamwork on page 7.)

A Divide into four teams: layout, lettering, colouring and imagery (the teacher might help you to do this). Write the names of each team member in the spaces below.

(a) The layout team:

_____

_____

(b) The lettering team:

_____

_____

(c) The colouring team:

_____

_____

(d) The imagery team:

_____

_____

> **Note:**
>
> Imagery: deciding on an image to complement the points made on the poster.
>
> Layout: working out how to place image and text on the page.

B Make two large posters for the classroom, one about good communication skills and the other about poor communication skills. Remember, each team member is to take part in compiling the poster. These posters can act as a reminder to everyone in the class to listen to each other.

My steps towards good communication

9 List some steps towards good communication that you have learned from the activity.

_____

_____

_____

_____

_____

> **Hint:**
> Have you mentioned body language, eye contact, active listening and being assertive?

MODULE 4

Physical health

It is essential that we look after our bodies if we want to live healthy and productive lives.

In this section, we look at the importance of maintaining good physical health.

Good physical health includes the following:

1. Healthy eating
2. Taking care of your body
3. Knowing the importance of rest and exercise
4. Let's get up and go

1. Healthy eating

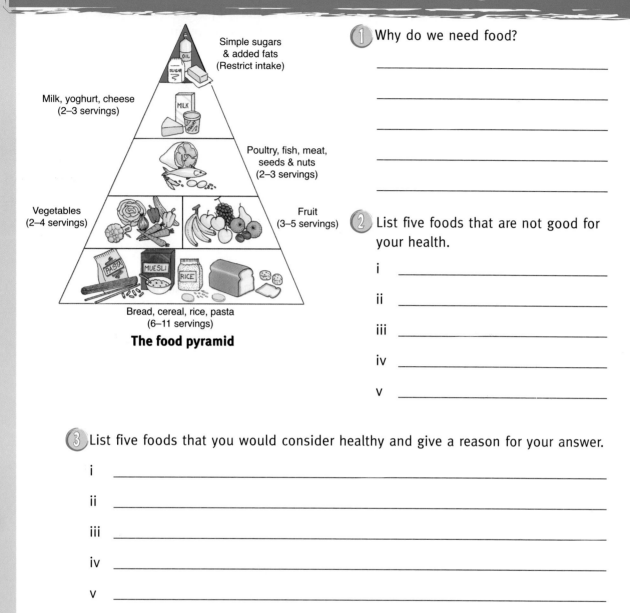

The food pyramid

1 Why do we need food?

_____

_____

_____

_____

_____

2 List five foods that are not good for your health.

i _____

ii _____

iii _____

iv _____

v _____

3 List five foods that you would consider healthy and give a reason for your answer.

i _____

ii _____

iii _____

iv _____

v _____

Nutrients

All foods are made up of nutrients. The type of nutrient found in the food will tell us whether or not the food is good for us. We need water and five different nutrient groups to continue to be healthy.

Types of food and nutrients

There are hundreds of different types of food available in the shops and we need to know which ones are best for us. All food labels will refer to the following:

Nutrient	Function	Source
Protein	◆ Growth and repair of cells. ◆ Produces hormones, enzymes and antibodies.	Meat, fish and eggs
Fats	◆ Heat and energy. ◆ Protection of delicate organs, e.g. heart. ◆ Provides vitamins A, D, E and K, which reduce blood clotting and reduce the effects of ageing.	Butter, cheese, meat, milk
Carbohydrates	◆ Heat and energy. ◆ Fibre. ◆ Growth and repair of cells.	Bread, cereal, rice, potatoes.
Vitamins and minerals (Vitamins A, D, E, K, B group and C)	◆ General good health	Fruit and vegetables

Nutrition Facts

Serving Size 1 Cup (28g/1.0 oz.)
Servings Per Container About 24

Amount Per Serving	Cereal	Cereal with ½ Cup Vitamins A&D Fat Free Milk
Calories	100	140
Calories from Fat	0	0
	% Daily Value**
Total Fat 0g*	0%	0%
Saturated Fat 0g	0%	0%
Trans Fat 0g		
Cholesterol 0mg	0%	0%
Sodium 200mg	8%	11%
Potassium 25mg	1%	7%
Total Carbohydrate 24g	8%	10%
Dietary Fibre 1g	4%	4%
Sugars 2g		
Other Carbohydrate 21g		
Protein 2g		
Vitamin A	10%	15%
Vitamin C	10%	10%
Calcium	0%	15%
Iron	45%	45%
Vitamin D	10%	25%
Thiamin	25%	30%
Riboflavin	25%	35%
Niacin	25%	25%
Vitamin B6	25%	25%
Folic Acid	25%	25%
Vitamin B12	25%	35%

* Amount in cereal. One half cup of fat free milk contributes an additional 40 calories, 65mg sodium, 6g total carbohydrate (6g sugars), and 4g protein.

**Percent Daily Values are based on a 2,000 calorie diet. Your daily values may be higher or lower depending on your calorie needs:

Cornflakes

Nutrition Facts

Serving Size ¾ Cup (31g/1.1 oz.)
Servings Per Container About 16

Amount Per Serving	Cereal	Cereal with ½ Cup Vitamins A&D Fat Free Milk
Calories	120	160
Calories from Fat	5	5
	% Daily Value**
Total Fat 0.5g*	1%	1%
Saturated Fat 0.5g	3%	3%
Trans Fat 0g		
Cholesterol 0mg	0%	0%
Sodium 180mg	8%	10%
Potassium 25mg	1%	7%
Total Carbohydrate 27g	9%	11%
Dietary Fibre 0g	0%	0%
Sugars 14g		
Other Carbohydrate 13g		
Protein 1g		
Vitamin A	10%	15%
Vitamin C	25%	25%
Calcium	0%	15%
Iron	25%	25%
Vitamin D	10%	25%
Thiamin	25%	30%
Riboflavin	25%	35%
Niacin	25%	25%
Vitamin B6	25%	25%
Folic Acid	25%	25%
Vitamin B12	25%	35%
Phosphorus	2%	15%

* Amount in cereal. One half cup of fat free milk contributes an additional 40 calories, 65mg sodium, 6g total carbohydrates (6g sugars), and 4g protein.

**Percent Daily Values are based on a 2,000 calorie diet. Your daily values may be higher or lower depending on your calorie needs:

Chocolate-based cereal

④ Look at the two food labels on page 26 and answer the following questions:

(a) How much vitamin C does the chocolate-based cereal contain?

_____

(b) How much protein is found in the cornflakes?

_____

(c) Which food provides the most fibre?

_____

(d) Which food do you think is the most healthy and why?

_____

⑤ Can you suggest ways to encourage a friend who doesn't like fruit to include more fruit in their diet?

_____

_____

_____

Water

Fact:
Our body is made up of two-thirds water and we need to replace it daily with up to eight glasses of water.

Soya and goat's milk are good alternatives for people with dairy allergies.

Fibre is needed to move food along the intestine.

Too much salt can cause high blood pressure and strokes.

⑥ In the space below, design a lunch menu for a teenager and give reasons why you have chosen the particular foods.

Menu	Reasons why

Helpful websites
http:/www.mypyramid.gov

2. Taking care of your body

What is personal hygiene?

Personal hygiene is very important to all of us.

Having good personal hygiene protects us from germs that grow and develop in sweat and dirt. We also smell nicer when we wash and this is important when we spend so much time with other people, e.g. in school or at home.

Did you know that on an average day humans produce one litre of sweat, which sticks to their skin? How many litres of sweat would stay on your skin if you did not wash for a week?

① Describe what would happen if you did not wash your skin or hair on a regular basis.

_____

_____

_____

Using a deodorant/anti-perspirant

② What is the difference between a deodorant and an anti-perspirant?

_____

_____

③ Can you name any deodorants/anti-perspirants that you can buy?

_____

_____

_____

_____

Clean Clothes

④ Why do you think it is important to put on clean underwear and clean clothes as part of your hygiene routine?

_____

_____

_____

_____

_____

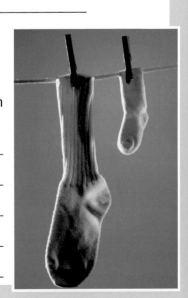

Your hair

5 Design an advertisement in the space below on how to look after your hair.

'Because I'm worth it' hair-care rules

Your skin

- Under the skin there are tiny oil and sweat glands.
- Oil and sweat appear on the surface of your skin through holes called pores.
- This can mix with dirt on your skin and block your pores.
- This can cause pimples, blackheads, boils and other skin infections.

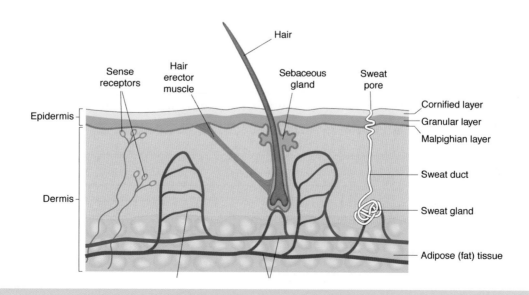

Teenagers and Skin

As a teenager, hormones can contribute to you having pimples or blackheads.

How can you help to prevent this from happening?

◆ Wash regularly with warm water and unperfumed soap.

◆ Always use your own clean face cloth, as bacteria like to hide in the fibres of the face cloth. Do you want to wash with someone else's bacteria?

◆ Avoid greasy food.

◆ Eat lots of fruit and vegetables and drink lots of water.

◆ Don't squeeze your spots – it will spread the infection.

◆ Keep your hands away from your face to avoid spreading the infection.

◆ Use special lotions or creams if you feel it is necessary. Can you name any?

◆ Dandruff can contribute towards spots and blackheads, so treat hair with special anti-dandruff shampoo.

Note:

Acne is a skin condition that causes a lot of spots which can easily become infected. This is very common during adolescence. Prescribed medicine (i.e. from your doctor) can help treat the problem.

> It is important to remember that nearly all adolescent boys and girls will get spots during puberty.

Your teeth

By the age of twelve most people have twenty-eight permanent teeth. There are still four more to come – our wisdom teeth.

How to look after your teeth

6 In the space below, list five ways to ensure that your teeth are healthy.

i _____

ii _____

iii _____

iv _____

v _____

3.Rest and exercise

Sleep

(1) Why do we sleep?

_____

_____

_____

(2) How much sleep is enough?

_____

_____

_____

(3) How would you feel if you didn't get enough sleep every night?

_____

_____

_____

DEPENDING ON YOUR AGE, YOU ARE LIKELY TO NEED MORE OR LESS SLEEP.

In general:

1. Babies need 21 hours a day.

2. Primary school children need 9–10 hours a day.

3. Teenagers also need 9–10 hours a day.

4. Adults need 8 hours a day.

With continued lack of sleep, the part of the brain that controls language, memory, planning and sense of time is severely affected, practically shutting down.

It is said that Napoleon, Florence Nightingale and Margaret Thatcher all slept for only four hours a night.

Thomas Edison claimed sleep was a waste of time.

OTHER ANIMAL SPECIES REQUIRE VARIED AMOUNTS OF SLEEP:

Pythons need 18 hours a day.

Tigers need 15.8 hours a day.

Cats need 12.1 hours a day.

Chimpanzees need 9.7 hours a day.

Sheep need 3.8 hours a day.

African elephants need 3.3 hours a day.

Giraffes need only 1.9 hours a day.

Everyone is different, so some people need less (or more) sleep than others.

4. Let's get up and go

Physical activity is as necessary for your body as rest and sleep.

1 What physical activity do you prefer?

_____

_____

_____

2 What physical activities do you dislike?

_____

_____

_____

3 Identify physical activities that you do at present.

_____

_____

_____

4 Why do you think that physical activity is important?

_____

_____

_____

5 In the left column of the box below, list the things that stop you from participating in physical activity. In the column beside it, outline how you might remedy/fix this.

Things that stop me participating in physical activity	What I can do to fix this

6 Outline the things that help you stay physically active.

_____

_____

Primary recommendations

- All young people should participate in physical activity of at least moderate intensity for one hour per day.

- Young people who currently do little activity should participate in physical activity of moderate intensity for at least 30 minutes per day.

Secondary recommendations

- At least twice a week, some of the activities should help enhance and maintain muscular strength, flexibility and bone health.

Regular physical activity means:

- Sport for 20 minutes, three times per week.

- Lifestyle activity for 30 minutes, three times per week, e.g. walking to school.

⑦ Fill in the table below for one week to see just how healthy you are:

HEALTH TABLE					Week 1 Date:_____			
	Exercise		Rest		Eating			
Day	Activity	Time Spent	Sleep	Rest	Breakfast	Lunch	Dinner	No. Of Snacks
Monday (*example*)	Walked to school	20 min	6 hours	1 hour TV	Cereal, toast, juice	Sandwich, apple, coke	Spaghetti bolognese	3
Monday								
Tuesday								
Wednesday								
Thursday								
Friday								
Saturday								
Sunday								

Well, how healthy are you . . . ?

(8) Have you had enough sleep for your age group?

_____

_____

(9) Have you met the primary recommendations for activity per day?

_____

_____

_____

(10) Compare your eating habits with the food pyramid on page 25.

_____

_____

_____

_____

_____

MODULE 5

Friendship

Friends are an important part of our lives.
This module looks at how to make new friends and the characteristics to look for in a good friend.

In this module you will find out about:

1 Making new friends

2 The characteristics of a good friend

1. Making new friends

1 What might your life be like if you had no friends?

Write a description or draw a picture of what this might be like in the box below.

- Throughout our lives, many people support us.

- They are our family and friends.

- Our lives revolve around our families when we are young.

- As we get older this circle of people expands to include our friends.

- Friends are very important as they are the people we choose to share our life experiences with.

② In the circles below, write the names of your family and friends.

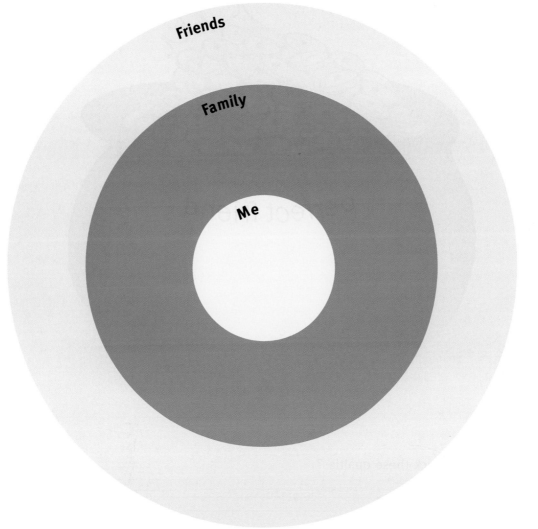

2. The characteristics of a good friend

Making friends is not always easy. The best way to approach it is to think about what makes a good friend.

Ad campaign

You are looking for the 'perfect' friend.

① Write an ad in your copybook for the local newspaper, outlining the type of friend you are looking for.

Which of the characteristics in the table below would you choose to make the 'perfect' friend?

Good looking	Patient	Kind	Popular
Trustworthy	Honest	Funny	Reliable
Wealthy	Loyal	Having shared interests	Being a good listener
Being able to say sorry		Respecting other people's feelings	

② Choose four qualities and place them in the pot below to create the perfect friend.

perfect friend

③ Why did you pick these qualties?

_____

_____

_____

Knowing what you want in a friend is just the start of the process. The next step is to make contact with such a person. Here are some suggestions:

◆ Make eye contact and wear a happy face. A smile can work wonders to make the other person feel at ease and to let them know that you are open to talk to.

◆ Try to be positive in your comments and manner. Nobody wants to talk to a moaner or someone with an angry face.

◆ Try out some ice-breaker lines, such as 'Did you see that programme on TV last night?' or 'What did you think of the match?'

◆ Try to come across as friendly. This will make people feel more willing to try to be friendly back.

Interview

Talk to the person next to you and find out about their best friend.

a) What is his/her name?

_____

b) What age is he/she?

_____

c) How did they meet him/her?

_____

_____

d) What made them like him/her at the beginning?

_____

_____

e) What do they like about him/her now?

_____

_____

f) What is his/her favourite colour?

_____

g) What is the nicest thing he/she has ever done for them?

_____

_____

h) Describe his/her family.

_____

_____

i) How would they feel if this person had to move to another country?

_____

_____

j) Are there any other questions you might like to ask?

_____

_____

Am I a good friend?

(1) I am a good friend because:

_____

_____

_____

(2) The qualities I have to offer as a friend are:

_____

_____

_____

(3) Ask one of your friends why they like you as a friend.

_____

_____

_____

> **Why is it important to be selective and to choose your friends wisely?**

ACTIVITY

Collage

Collect some magazines and newspapers and create a collage which describes your best friend in words, pictures and colours.

MODULE 6

Relationships and sexuality education

In this module we look at the changes that occur during adolescence.
We will look at the emotional, physical and psychological development that occurs during puberty.

You will learn about:

1. Puberty: what is it?

2. Changes that occur during adolescence

3. The reproductive system

4. Respecting yourself and others

5. Gender stereotyping

1. Puberty: what is it?

Puberty is a time of change in your body and a time when your feelings and emotions can also change.

A number of physical changes also occur during this time for both boys and girls.

① In the space below, list the changes that you have noticed from when you were 5 years old to now.

_____

_____

_____

_____

_____

_____

_____

When does puberty happen?

Everybody is unique, so puberty begins at different times for each person. For most people, it begins between the ages of 10 and 16. However, it can start earlier or later.

Why does puberty happen?

Puberty is the beginning of sexual maturity. Once puberty begins, reproduction is possible. Hormones are released into the bloodstream to help bring about these changes. The pituitary gland (a small gland found in the brain) is responsible for causing the release of oestrogen and progesterone in females and testosterone in males.

2. Changes that occur during adolescence

Puberty in females

Many changes happen within your body. Some are visible, and some are not.

- Change in body shape.

- The hip bone widens.

- Periods (menstruation) begin.

- Hormone oestrogen is released.

- Breasts develop and become larger.

- Pubic and underarm hair begins to grow.

- Acne can appear on the face and neck.

- The vaginal wall will thicken.

ACTIVITY

Identify the changes that occur during puberty in females on the diagram to the left.

Puberty in males

For boys, many changes happen during puberty. Some are visible and some are not.

- Shoulders, arms and legs increase in size.

- Voice deepens.

- Pubic, underarm and facial hair grow.

- Acne can develop on face and neck.

- Growth spurt.

- Testicles get larger.

- The testes start to produce sperm.

ACTIVITY

Identify the changes that occur during puberty in males on the diagram to the left.

3. The reproductive system

Teacher's Manual

Female reproduction

ACTIVITY

Use the information in the table below to label the diagram of the female reproductive organs.

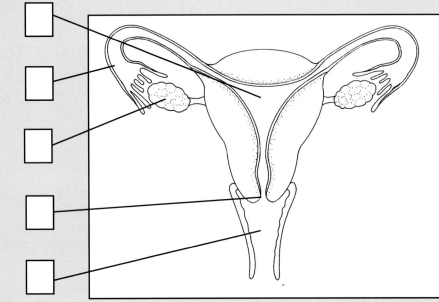

Female reproductive organs		What they do
1	Ovaries	Most females have two ovaries. Both produce eggs. Each is about the size of a large strawberry.
2	Fallopian tubes	There are two fallopian tubes. These connect the ovaries and the uterus in order to carry the eggs from the ovaries to the uterus. They are about as wide as a drinking straw.
3	Uterus/womb	The uterus (or womb as it is called when a woman is pregnant) is a hollow muscle that increases in size to hold a foetus. It connects to the fallopian tubes and the vagina. It is about the size and shape of a pear.
4	Cervix	The cervix is the opening at the lower end of the uterus and this stretches when a baby is ready to be born.
5	Vagina	This is the connection between the uterus and the outside of the body.

Ovulation

Most females have a 'fertile period' when ovulation occurs. Ovulation usually happens from Day 11 to 17 of the menstrual cycle (counting the first day of the period as Day 1). This is when an egg is released (which can live up to 48 hours). If the egg meets the sperm (which can live up to 72 hours), it is possible to become pregnant.

However, it is possible to get pregnant at any time – and especially during adolescence – as menstrual cycles can change from month to month. Some months can be shorter and others longer. Therefore, it is difficult to know exactly when ovulation occurs.

Menstruation

Menstruation is when the lining of the womb breaks down and is released through the vagina. When girls menstruate, it is usually referred to as 'having a period'.

Questions

1 *How long will my periods last?*
The average length of bleeding will last between three to six days, depending on the individual.

2 *Do boys have periods?*
No.

3 *Will my period hurt?*
For some people it can hurt. For others, it doesn't. If you do find periods painful, some gentle exercise can help to relieve the cramps.

4 *What is PMT?*
PMT stands for 'pre-menstrual tension', which some people get a few days before their periods are due. This can cause the body to retain water, the person to feel more emotional than usual and experience cravings for high-sugar foods.

5 *Will other people know when I have my period?*
Not unless you choose to tell them.

6 *How will I tell my parents?*
Pick an appropriate time (maybe when no one else is in the room). Keep in mind that your mother has experienced this and your father knows all about it too, so try not to feel embarrassed. You may have already had a discussion with your parents about it before your periods started. This would be the time to ask your mother to buy tampons or sanitary towels for you.

7 *Which sanitary products are better – tampons or sanitary towels?*
Again, it is not a case of which product is better, but which you feel comfortable using. It is probably best to try both and see how you feel. Both will give instructions on how to use them on the packets.

8 *What will I do if I get my period in school?*
It is a good idea to keep some sanitary protection in your bag. Some schools will have towel/tampon dispensers: if your school hasn't got one of these, ask a female teacher you know and she will be able to help you.

9 *Can I have a bath?*
Of course, and, if you suffer period pains, this might help you relax. Hygiene is very important during your period. You should shower/bathe daily.

Male reproduction

ACTIVITY

Use the information in the table below to label the diagram of the male reproductive organs.

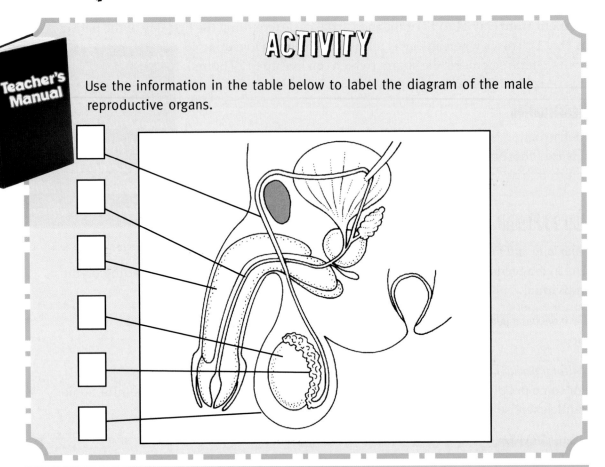

	Male reproductive organs	What they do
1	Scrotum	This is a sac of wrinkly skin that holds the testicles.
2	Penis	This is made of spongy tissue and blood vessels. A small opening at the top of the penis allows urine out of the body. When a penis becomes stiff and stands out from the body this is called an 'erection'.
3	Testis	This is where the sperm is produced. A boy has two testicles and each is about the size of a walnut.
4	Epididymis	This is a small tube-like structure that stores the sperm.
5	Vas deferens (sperm duct)	This is the connection between the urethra and the outside of the body.
6	Urethra	This is a long narrow tube which is found in the penis and carries urine from the body. Semen also leaves the body through the urethra.

Questions

1. *What is an erection?*
   This is when the soft tissues of your penis fill with blood and become hard and erect. Erections will normally happen when a boy is sexually excited.

2. *Will everyone know that I have an erection?*
   Not always.

3. *What is a wet dream?*
   It is when you ejaculate involuntarily in your sleep. This can occur especially during puberty.

4. *What is ejaculation?*
   Ejaculation is when semen which contains sperm is released from the body. During sexual intercourse this is released inside the vagina.

5. *Will ejaculation happen every time a boy has an erection?*
   No.

6. *How many sperm are found in an ejaculation?*
   Like everything else, each person is different, but it is possible to estimate that the average ejaculation will contain between 50–150 million sperm.

4. Respecting yourself and others

Making love

So now you have seen that your body develops physically during your teenage years. Believe it or not, you are not only changing physically but spiritually, emotionally and mentally. You are slowly becoming an adult. When you become an adult and you are in a long-term, loving relationship, you and your partner may want to show the strength of your feelings for each other by making love (having sexual intercourse). Before having a sexual relationship it is important that both adults have a respect, trust and understanding of each other. When making love, a baby can be conceived. The age of consent for sexual intercourse in Ireland is 16 years for heterosexuals and 17 years for homosexuals. It is important to remember that while it may be legal to have sexual intercourse, this doesn't mean that a person is emotionally and psychologically ready for such a relationship.

Signpost ➲

You will also be learning about this subject in your Home Economics class.

1. List some stories or myths used by adults to explain conception or pregnancy.

   _____

   _____

   _____

   _____

◆ Conception occurs when the male sperm join the female egg in the fallopian tube to form a foetus.

◆ This bunch of cells travels down to the uterus after a couple of days and grows into a baby over the next 40 weeks.

◆ Once conception has taken place the characteristics that make each of us unique are formed – colour of our hair, eyes, our gender, our height.

◆ Throughout the pregnancy the developing baby is totally dependent on the mother to protect it and to provide nourishment.

5. Gender stereotyping

◆ Stereotyping occurs when people are categorised according to their religion, the colour of their skin, their nationality, etc.

◆ Gender stereotyping occurs when someone is categorised according to their sex – male or female. This can often be negative and create discrimination between the sexes.

Note
Gender refers to a person being male or female, having masculine or feminine traits.

◆ Gender roles refer to the type of behaviour expected from men and women within society. Some of the most common stereotypes are of a woman staying at home to mind the children and care for the house while the man goes to work, or women as being weak and men being strong.

◆ Children observe adult stereotypes from a very early age, from the type/colour of clothes they wear to the toys they are allowed to play with.

① 'Big boys don't cry.'

Do you agree with this statement? Why or why not?

_____

_____

_____

_____

The following words are in the word puzzle below. Can you find all of them? Write the letter 'M' beside words you associate with being male and 'F' beside those you associate with being female.

	M or F			M or F
aggressive	_____	compassionate	_____
gullible	_____	tender	_____
cheerful	_____	feminine	_____
affectionate	_____	competitive	_____
dominant	_____	sensitive	_____
independent	_____	gentle	_____
brainy	_____		

C	C	D	V	K	Y	L	G	C	B	G	Q	O
O	O	O	J	Z	C	H	E	E	R	F	U	L
M	U	M	I	A	W	M	N	R	A	J	P	C
P	J	I	P	B	Z	F	T	A	I	A	N	E
E	R	N	D	A	X	X	L	B	N	H	S	N
T	D	A	F	N	S	H	E	L	Y	A	C	I
I	P	N	I	C	F	S	O	C	K	T	A	N
T	Q	T	G	U	L	L	I	B	L	E	R	I
I	T	E	N	D	E	R	U	O	P	B	Q	M
V	A	F	F	E	C	T	I	O	N	A	T	E
E	E	V	I	T	I	S	N	E	S	A	D	F
R	I	N	D	E	P	E	N	D	E	N	T	R
A	G	G	R	E	S	S	I	V	E	E	A	E

To help you really understand stereotyping, try the following quiz:

True or false?

◆ Boys are better at sport than girls _____

◆ Boys never wear make-up _____

◆ Mothers are better at minding children than fathers _____

◆ Women don't drive as well as men _____

◆ Housework is for girls _____

◆ Women are better at cooking than men _____

◆ Men cannot do housework _____

Stereotyping can sometimes be explained by how we are brought up and what our culture and society tells us is 'normal'.

ACTIVITY

In groups, make an information leaflet about the facts that you have discovered in this module that you feel might help other teenagers understand the changes that are happening to them now.

Using the information in this chapter, create a bank of questions and answers that could be used in an end-of-school-year table quiz on SPHE.

Signpost ⊃

What you learn in Module 5 (Friendship) and Module 7 (Emotional Health) will be helpful to you in this module.

Did you know that in Ireland until the 1970s women working in the civil service and banks had to retire on getting married?!

MODULE 7

Emotional health

Life involves experiencing a wide range of emotions.
We describe our daily experiences as 'good days' and 'bad days', based on our strongest emotion for the day. Being able to identify our emotions helps us to express them appropriately.

Consideration for our own emotional health and that of others is explored under the two headings:

1 Recognising feelings/emotions

2 Respecting your feelings and the feelings of others

1. Recognising feelings/emotions

Defining Emotion

The Oxford English Dictionary (second edition, 2003) defines 'feeling' as: **noun 1** an emotional state or reaction: *a feeling of joy*; (feelings) the emotional side of someone's character: *I don't want to hurt her feelings*; **2** an idea or belief: *he had the feeling that he was being watched*; **3** the capacity to experience the sense of touch.

'Emotion' is defined as **noun 1** a strong feeling deriving from one's circumstances, mood or relationships with others.

These meanings highlight how many feelings come from the outside (the people we meet, places we go, music we hear) to the feelings we have on the inside (having a crush on somebody, feeling lonely). To help manage all this emotion it might be helpful to learn a relaxation exercise before we go any further.

ACTIVITY

(at home or in school)

Throughout our lives we need to know how to relax, and one way of doing this is through meditation. Meditation can help us become aware of our emotions and can also help us to move from one emotion to another, e.g. from feeling angry to feeling calm.

Allow 15 to 20 minutes. Try it once at least and see how you feel!!!

The following 10 steps might help you to relax:

1. Sit in a quiet room, with some gentle background music or some incense burning.
2. Place feet flat on the ground (remove your shoes if you want) or lay down on a mat on the floor.
3. Breathe in and out slowly and deeply – iiiiinnn oooouuut – listen to your breathing and close your eyes.
4. Concentrate on your breathing, in and out.
5. Now, very slowly, tense your toes and feet; hold for ten seconds, then relax.
6. Relax your toes.
7. Repeat parts 5 and 6 for all parts of your body – legs, back, stomach, hands, arms, shoulders, neck and face.
8. When you have completed part 7, your body should feel relaxed and free from any tension.
9. Continue listening to the music/silence.
10. When you are ready, open your eyes slowly and sit up.

⚡ Remember fire safety when using matches or candles.

In your copybook, write out the times you feel that doing the above exercise would help you become aware of / change how you were feeling.

Getting in touch with our feelings

Feeling good and happy is what we strive for in life, but the journey involves experiencing the variety of emotions that life brings.

Getting in touch with how feelings work and why we have them can help us greatly to learn how best to express these emotions.

The four basic emotions are:
Anger, fear, sadness and happiness

ACTIVITY

Try to identify as many emotions as you can that fall under the four basic emotions.

Circle the emotion in the colour of the main emotion as illustrated below.

You may find some words can be circled with a few different colours.

Anger   **Fear**   **Sadness**   **Happiness**

Guilt   DISTRESS   Appreciated   Strained   Frustrated

Loved   LONESOME

Panic   Irritated

Satisfied   Courageous   Terror   Worried   Gloomy

Tense   Resentful   Excited

PRESSURISED   Annoyed   Doubtful   Thrilled

Vulnerable   Provoked

Affectionate

Anxious   Delighted   Alarmed

Respected   Miserable   Enthusiastic

Apprehensive

Aggressive   Upset

Mixed up   Disappointed

53

Compare your circling with the person beside you. Did you both agree to which type of emotion each word belonged?

List or draw some of the emotions that you have experienced as part of growing up. These emotions may not have been on the list.

2. Respecting your feelings and the feelings of others

Anger

Anger is not just about aggressive behaviour. In fact, anger is not always a negative emotion. It is what makes us stand up for ourselves; without anger we would let people treat us as they wished. Anger helps us to protect our beliefs and our selves. Indeed, some of the most effective activists acted out of anger for the good of humanity.

**Martin Luther King, Jr
(1929–1968)**

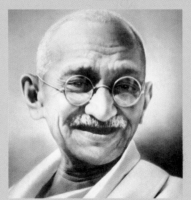
**Mahatma Gandhi
(1869–1948)**

**Bob Geldof
(1951–)**

Dealing with anger

Anger is a strong emotion, so it is important to remember that it is your responsibility to handle it correctly. Sometimes your anger might be justified, but other times you may, in fact, be wrong. Therefore, being honest with yourself as to why you are angry allows you the time to think before you act out of anger. If you are wrong, you can try to work on feelings of anger by taking a few deep breaths to release the tension. This can help prevent an argument. If the other person is wrong, then you can give the person the chance to explain or to do something about it.

Once you learn to identify that you are angry and what caused you to feel that way, it becomes easier to let the anger go and move on. In this way, you control your anger instead of it controlling you.

ACTIVITY

Can you suggest safe ways to 'work off anger' in the suggestion box below?

SUGGESTION BOX

◆ Count to ten; this will give you time to think before you react.

◆ Talk to someone about why you feel angry, e.g. a friend or sibling.

◆ Take five deep breaths.

◆ _____

◆ _____

◆ _____

◆ _____

◆ _____

Growing up

Strong feelings are normal. The teenage years bring more challenges to test how you deal with good and bad feelings. As you grow older, you become better at knowing how to handle your feelings and how to respect the feelings of others.

1 Describe a time when you had difficulty dealing with a particular bad feeling. What made it so difficult? What method did you use to cope with the feeling?

_____

_____

_____

2 How would you help someone else to handle the same feeling?

_____

_____

_____

Signpost ⊃

What you have learned in Module 3 (Communication skills) will be useful to you in this module.

ACTIVITY

In the World Cup Final 2006 in Berlin, the French footballer Zinedine Zidane was given the red card for head-butting Italy's Marco Materazzi. Zidane claims he reacted to an insult by Materazzi concerning his family.

Do you think this is an appropriate expression of anger?

_____

_____

Collect headlines of any such public expressions of emotions in the news.

Sadness

Another strong emotion we feel is sadness. Sadness is the emotion that helps us to grieve. It helps to relieve some of the distress of losing something or someone close to us. It is very important to give ourselves time when we experience sadness; it can help us begin to accept our loss.

'Death leaves a heartache no one can heal, love leaves a memory no one can steal.'
From a gravestone in Ireland

GROUP ACTIVITY

Class discussion

A) What can make people feel sad?

_____

_____

B) What steps can we take when we are feeling sad?

_____

_____

C) Can you recall and describe a time when you felt sad?

_____

_____

_____

D) What helped you through that time of sadness?

_____

_____

E What support would you give to a friend in a time of sadness?

_____

_____

_____

Fear

Fear is another active emotion. When we are frightened, our muscles tense up and our bodies make small twitches. This is our body's way of gearing up towards the 'fight or flight' response.

What do we mean by 'fight or flight'?

When an animal is threatened or frightened, it has two options:
It can stay and fight, or it can run away in flight.
Either way, it has to muster up as much energy as it can to defend itself in fight or run as fast as it can to escape in flight.

Our body's reaction to fear

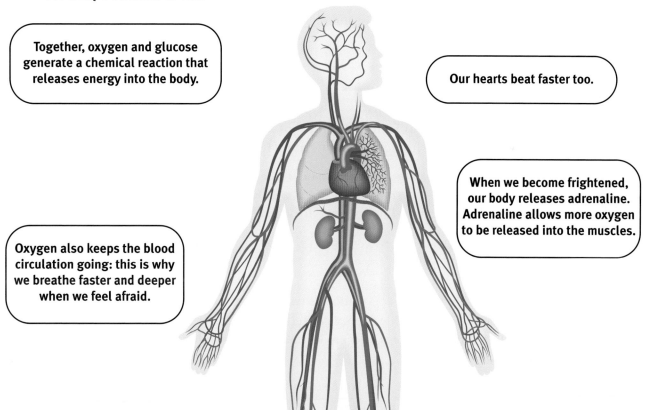

Together, oxygen and glucose generate a chemical reaction that releases energy into the body.

Our hearts beat faster too.

When we become frightened, our body releases adrenaline. Adrenaline allows more oxygen to be released into the muscles.

Oxygen also keeps the blood circulation going: this is why we breathe faster and deeper when we feel afraid.

Common Fears

◆ Coming last, getting the lowest grade in the class, failing.
◆ Making mistakes, being wrong.
◆ Being rejected or left out.
◆ Embarrassment.

③ What suggestions do you have to help overcome fears?

_____

_____

_____

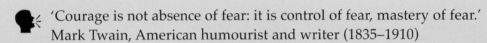 ' I have learnt over the years that when one's mind is made up, this diminishes fear; knowing what must be done does away with fear.'
Rosa Parks, African-American civil rights activist (1913–2005)

Fear is a very necessary emotion for physical self-protection in dangerous situations. It serves us at times when we feel threatened by other people or unfamiliar environments. Feelings of fear remind us to take precautions and to behave safely.

Learning from Fear

ACTIVITY

Describe your most memorable experience of fear to the person beside you.

Explain how you felt physically and mentally. What did you do to overcome the feeling of fear?

'Courage is not absence of fear: it is control of fear, mastery of fear.'
Mark Twain, American humourist and writer (1835–1910)

The tragedy of 9/11, the destruction of the World Trade Centre in New York, saw ordinary people become heroes. These people acted to save others despite their own fear. These heroes have shown how it is possible to move forward beyond fear.

Stress

When faced with non-physical threats – such as worrying about an exam or being late for a meeting – we have no outlet for the energy caused by this fear. If it becomes a continuous fear, it can lead to feelings of stress and anxiety that can have long-term effects on our health and wellbeing.

A simple relaxation exercise, like the exercise on page 52, can help reduce the pent-up feeling of stress. It only takes ten minutes.

ACTIVITY

Research the effects of stress on the body, and ways to reduce stress in our lives. Make posters or pamphlets to distribute this information in your school.

Happiness

Happiness is a very positive feeling. Experience of the previously mentioned emotions makes us truly appreciate the 'feel-good' feeling of happiness. We experience happiness when we feel our needs are being met – such as feeling loved, cared for and safe.

Happiness is found in a wide variety of activities, so much so that people seem to take these for granted.

Common things that make people happy are:

♦ Feeling of self-worth, feeling that we are capable of doing something.

♦ Feeling that we can give or do good deeds for others.

♦ Spending time on a hobby or an exciting activity can trigger the feeling also.

♦ Other pursuits involve listening to music or enjoying nature.

ACTIVITY

In your copybook, make a picture of one of the previously discussed emotions. Collect pictures, words and phrases that are typical of that emotion. Select colours that emphasise the emotion. See if people can guess which emotion you chose.

How would you feel?

Many teenagers feel that they stand out as being different and this can make them feel quite lonely. Difficulties occur when other people will not accept or respect a person for their difference.

4 What difficulties do you think young people face these days?

_____

_____

_____

5 To help people through a difficult time, you can show you care with the simplest gestures. Add to the list of suggestions below.

Smile. _____

Say hello. _____

Offer your help. _____

Look at the pictures and fill in the thought bubbles to describe how you think each character might feel.

1. **Boy on his own in playground being ignored by other students.**

2. **Girl being applauded by students on receipt of a sports award.**

3. **Boy being complimented by friends on his new shoes.**

4. **Girl coming out of school to find her bike damaged.**

 'Nobody can make you feel inferior without your consent.'

Eleanor Roosevelt, American politician and wife
of President Franklin D. Roosevelt (1884–1962)

MODULE 8

Influences and decisions

Reviewing how we are influenced by people we meet and the people we hear about will give us a better understanding of how we make decisions in our lives.

We experience this influence from a very early age from our family, friends and culture. As we grow older we become more aware of the media's influence and the effect it has on our decisions.

This module looks at this process under the headings:

1 Influences and how we make decisions

2 Decision-making

3 My heroes

4 Be yourself

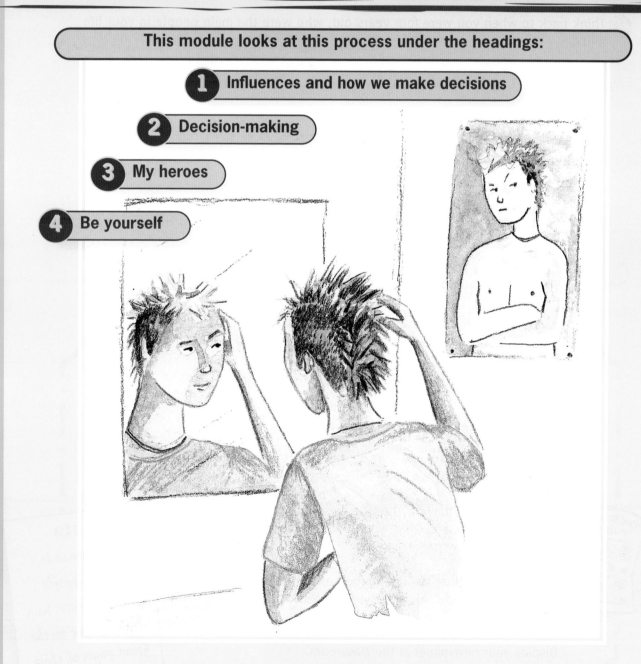

1. Influences and how we make decisions

Throughout our lives various people will have an effect on the decisions we make. This is referred to as someone 'influencing' you.

1 Discuss how young people can be influenced in the decisions they make under the following headings:

- Sporting activities
- Friendships
- Responsibility
- Sense of dress
- Relationships
- Behaviour
- Personal grooming

2 Think back to when you were four years old; who were the main people in your life and why?

_____

_____

_____

3 When you were twelve years old, who did you listen to the most and why?

_____

_____

_____

4 Do you still listen to this person the most? Why or why not?

_____

_____

ACTIVITY

Newspaper

Find someone in history who has made a difference to you or who has done something you admire or respect.

What are the qualities and achievements of this person that you would like to include in your newspaper?

Gather the information and then make up the front page of a newspaper using the information, photos, etc. you have collected.

Display your newspaper in the classroom.

Note

Look at the wide variety of people your classmates have chosen to put on the front pages of their newspapers.

ACTIVITY

Ian is in a music shop with his friend. His friend wants him to put a CD in his bag without paying.

Write what you think the people below would say to him in that situation:

His parents	
His older sister	
His teacher	
A well-known football personality	
A rock star	
His best friend	
The police	
Ian himself	

Why, in your opinion, do people let other people influence their behaviour?

_____

_____

_____

_____

2. Decision-making

From the moment we wake up in the morning until we go to bed at night, we constantly have to make decisions. The decisions can be as simple as deciding to stay in bed 10 minutes after the alarm clock has gone off, or can be as important as deciding to complete your Junior Certificate exam.

Our decisions can be influenced by our family and friends as well as by our goals, values and dreams. Many decisions we make can be influenced by what we believe in, e.g. religious beliefs, morals and values.

It is vital to remember that all the decisions we make will have consequences and that we have to be able to accept responsibility for these when they happen.

> **Note**
>
> Decision-making means making a choice between two or more options.

Sometimes we might make a wrong decision and it is important to acknowledge this and take responsibility for it.

The decision-making process

The process of decision-making involves the following steps:

1. Defining the decision – what is the decision?
2. Collecting and gathering the information – from where can I get information?
3. Considering the possible options – two or more options may be available to you.
4. Considering the consequences of each option.
5. Deciding on an option.
6. Carrying out the decision made.
7. Evaluating the decision process – was it the right decision? Why or why not?

Apply the decision-making process to the following situations:

1. Mary is 14 years old and has been asked to attend a party on Thursday night. She knows her parents wouldn't approve as it is a school night and the party is at her best friend's older sister's house. Mary really wants to go. What should she do?

_____

_____

_____

_____

2. John has been offered some drugs by some of his friends in school. John knows the effects taking drugs can have on a person as his older cousin is a drug addict. John wants to fit in with his friends' plans, but doesn't really want to take the drugs. What should he do?

_____

_____

_____

_____

3. My heroes

Pop stars, movies stars, sports stars: these people are often called heroes. Why?

List some personalities that you would regard as your heroes and say why.

Hero	Why?

ACTIVITY

In the space below, write a magazine article about your hero, saying why they are your hero (you can include a picture if you like). Mention the skills or talents they have that you particularly admire. Remember, your hero can be someone you know; heroes do not only appear in magazines!

My hero is . . .

People I influence

Not only do people influence us, but we also influence other people. If you have a younger brother or sister (or a younger cousin), they probably look to you for guidance or direction. You may also influence your friends and/or your classmates.

ACTIVITY

In the space below, list the people you influence:

_____

_____

Why do you think you influence them?

_____

_____

How can you be a positive influence on other people?

_____

_____

4. Be yourself

Draw an outline of your hand in the box on the following page and colour it in. You can get someone to help you if you like.

1 Show your drawing to the class: how is it different from your classmates' drawings?

_____

_____

_____

2 Can you imagine what the world would be like if everyone was the same, i.e. if everyone looked the same and liked the same things? How would you feel?

_____

_____

_____

3 Would you want to be different or the same? Why?

_____

_____

_____

My hand

What are your individual qualities? Write your name in the middle of the space below and surround your name with words that describe your qualities.

Use fancy lettering, colours and decorate it as much as possible.

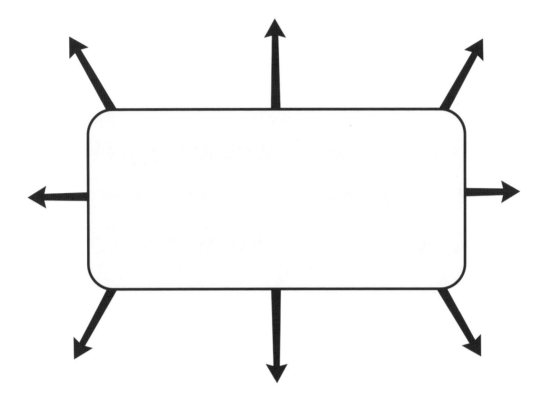

5) Do you think the whole class will have the same qualities? Why or why not?

_____

_____

_____

_____

Peer Pressure

During adolescence, our friends in school can influence us more than anyone else. This can be positive or negative and is sometimes referred to as peer pressure. As a result of this, some teenagers are afraid to show their differences or their individuality because they are afraid of being mocked.

ACTIVITY

Why do you think that during adolescence some people want to be the same and fit in?
Make a list of the positive and negative effects of trying to fit in.

Positive	Negative

ACTIVITY

Read the letter below from Andrew to Agony Aunt Dora.

Dear Dora,
I love classical music and have been playing piano and violin since I was three. I recently won a national competition which is going to be televised. My friends in school think I like heavy metal music. I am afraid of what my classmates will say/do when they find out I'm different.
Andrew

Write your answer to Andrew in the space below:

Dear Andrew,

Carry out research in your class by asking the following questions and recording the results.

A First, find out the number of students who:

Play football

_____

Listen to U2

_____

REMEMBER EVERYONE IS UNIQUE, AND THEIR LIKES, DISLIKES, HOPES AND DREAMS ARE DIFFERENT.

Like going to school

_____

B Then find out the number of students who want to:

Be famous

_____

Go to college

_____

Get married

_____

Enjoy swimming

_____

Leave school

_____

Travel the world

_____

Like doing homework

_____

C If your best friend has different likes/beliefs to you, will he or she still remain your best friend? Why or why not?

_____

_____

_____

MODULE 9

Substance Use

In this module we will look at different types of legal and illegal drugs and how they can affect our bodies.

Substance use will be explored under the following headings:

1 What is a drug?

2 Alcohol

3 Solvents

4 Smoking and its effects

SMOKE FREE ZONE

1. What is a Drug?

A drug is any chemical substance, other than food, that changes the way a person's body works and the way a person acts and feels.

What do we mean by substance use?

When used in the correct way, drugs can help to prolong life and cure disease. As you will see, however, if drugs are misused they can cause psychological, emotional, physical and social problems – and can even result in death.

Who uses drugs?

Most of us at some stage in our lives will use a drug:

1. If we are unwell a doctor may prescribe medication to help us get better.
2. If we have a cup of tea or coffee in the morning, or a can of Coca-Cola at lunch.
3. If we have a headache or period pain, we might take a mild painkiller to ease the discomfort.

When adults drink alcohol or smoke cigarettes, they are taking chemicals into their bodies. Some sports people use performance-enhancing drugs – for example stimulants, growth hormones and anabolic steroids. The Olympic Council of Ireland has a list of restricted drugs and many sports people have lost medals due to the use of these banned drugs.

a) The power of medicine

Medicine refers to any drug or remedy for use in treating, preventing or alleviating the symptoms of infection and disease. Common diseases can still kill people today.

Life in 2007

Sam lives in Niger with his eight brothers and sisters. Last year two of his brothers died after contracting the measles virus. His family didn't have the money to be immunised. Sam now has measles and is afraid he will die.

Sarah lives in Ireland. She has one brother who has never had the measles. Yesterday when Sarah woke up she had a red rash all over her body. Her mum says she has the measles and will have to stay at home from school all week.

Why do you think Sam's quality of life is so different from Sarah's?

_____

_____

_____

b) Different types of medicine

There are many different forms of medicine and different types of doctors or medical practitioners. You go to your GP (general practitioner) if you have a sore throat or persistent pain. You may be referred to a specialist if you have an illness that requires more in-depth treatment. You might be treated by a physiotherapist for a sports injury. You will go to a surgeon if you need an operation and an anaesthetist for a general anaesthetic.

More often today, some people are seeking out other forms of medicine: many people go to complementary practitioners – for instance, acupuncturists or homeopaths – for alternatives to traditional medicine.

 Can you draw arrows to link the type of doctor you might go to with the following ailments:

A broken ankle?   Dermatologist

Psoriasis?   GP

A tummy bug?   Cardiologist

A heart complaint?   Orthopaedist

c) Misuse of drugs

Legal drugs

As you know, legal drugs include:

- Medicines – drugs available from your doctor on prescription or over the counter, such as painkillers – for example, aspirin.

- Socially acceptable drugs – drugs such as alcohol and cigarettes, which can cause a lot of harm to people and families. People can become addicted to both alcohol and nicotine.

- Drugs found in food such as tea, coffee, chocolate and cola drinks. These all contain a high percentage of caffeine which can cause a person to be irritable, fidgety and nervous.

- Other substances found at home, e.g. aerosols and adhesives, are easily obtained but can cause death when inhaled.

Both legal and illegal drugs can be harmful to the body. Excess of many legal drugs (for instance, alcohol or prescription drugs) can cause people to become very ill and even die.

Illegal drugs

Misuse of illegal drugs can be very damaging. It can lead to emotional, physical and social problems for the individual and society.

- ♦ Illegal drugs are those drugs that have been identified by law as unsuitable for human use – for instance, cannabis or heroin, which are available on the black market.

- ♦ You will find out later in this chapter why they have been identified as unsuitable for human use.

③ Do you agree with the reasons below why some people misuse drink and drugs?

Reason	Agree	Disagree
Everybody is doing it		
Curiosity		
Drugs help people forget problems at home and at school		
Drugs are enjoyable		
Drugs can help people cope with stress		

Drink and drug misuse can lead to:

- ♦ Vandalism.
- ♦ Aggression.
- ♦ Accidental death, e.g. drowning.
- ♦ Shoplifting.
- ♦ Burglary.
- ♦ Absenteeism from school and work.
- ♦ Getting into trouble with the gardaí.
- ♦ Psychological and emotional problems.

2. Alcohol

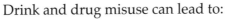

Alcohol is a legal drug. In Ireland (as in many other countries), drinking alcohol is associated with many social events.

However, as with other drugs, misuse of alcohol can lead to many problems.

Most people who use alcohol drink it in moderation. These people are often called social drinkers. However, when alcohol is misused, it can lead to social, physical, mental and emotional problems. This is when alcoholism creeps in.

1. Can you recall any campaigns on the TV that highlight the effects of alcoholism?

_____

_____

_____

_____

Alcoholism

- ◆ It is estimated that about 10 per cent of all drinkers become addicted to alcohol.

- ◆ They are called alcoholics.

- ◆ Alcoholics become dependent on alcohol, both physically and mentally.

- ◆ This means that they crave alcohol and that once they start drinking they find it very hard to stop. They cannot 'take it or leave it'.

- ◆ For an alcoholic, 'one drink is too many, a hundred is never enough.'

- ◆ Often, alcoholics neglect their work and families in order to feed their addiction.

- ◆ The only known cure for alcoholism is to stop drinking.

- ◆ Many towns in Ireland have support groups for alcoholics (Alcoholics Anonymous) or for their families (Al Anon or Alateen).

- ◆ People of all ages and backgrounds can develop alcoholism.

- ◆ The World Health Organisation recognises alcoholism as the third biggest killer disease globally.

Why do people misuse alcohol?

1. Some people who misuse alcohol do so because they believe that alcohol will help them to relax. However, the effect will only be temporary and will not replace other forms of relaxation – for instance, going for a walk or meditating.

2. People who misuse alcohol often do so to avoid facing feelings they may have. All of us will feel sad or angry at times: some alcohol users would prefer not to face these feelings and avoid them by getting an artificial feeling of wellbeing (a 'high').

Why do teenagers misuse alcohol?

1. Peer pressure.

2. Curiosity.

3. Compensation for low self-esteem.

> **Helpful websites**
> www.al-anon-ireland.org
> www.alcoholicsanonymous.ie

Problem of dependence

1. Unfortunately, for drugs users, the feelings of wellbeing that they strive for when using drugs are temporary. When they stop using drugs, they can, in fact, feel worse because they still have to face the feelings they have avoided. This can lead to depression and anxiety.

2. In addition, drug users can build up a tolerance for the substance they are using. This means that if they want to repeat the same feeling of wellbeing, they must increase the amount of the drug they are using.

(3) Drug users can become dependent on and addicted to a drug – this can mean they find it difficult to stop using the drug. If they want to stop they may have to go 'cold turkey' or go to rehabilitation.

How alcohol abuse affects the user and other people

(1) How might alcohol abuse affect the individual?

_____

_____

(2) How might alcohol abuse affect the family?

_____

_____

(3) How might alcohol abuse affect society?

_____

_____

3. Solvents

What is solvent use?

- It is illegal to sell a solvent to a person under 18 if the shop assistant suspects the person will misuse the product.
- Solvent use involves the inhaling of gases, chemical fumes and vapours and is extremely dangerous. This is because it can kill a person very quickly.
- Nearly all abused inhalants produce effects that are similar to anaesthetics; they slow down the body's functions.
- If inhaled through the mouth or nose into the lungs, inhalants can cause intoxicating effects. Intoxication may last a few minutes or several hours if the inhalants are taken repeatedly. At first, users can feel slightly stimulated. With more inhalations, they may feel less inhibited and less in control. Finally, a user can lose consciousness.

The dangers of solvent use

Sniffing highly concentrated amounts of the chemicals in solvents or aerosol sprays can cause heart failure and death. High concentrations of inhalants can also cause death from suffocation by displacing oxygen in the lungs and then in the central nervous system so that breathing stops.

Death from inhalants

Usually, death from inhaling solvents is caused by a very high concentration of fumes. Deliberately inhaling from an attached paper or plastic bag, or in a closed area, greatly increases the chances of suffocation. Even when using substances for their legitimate purposes (for instance, painting, cleaning), it is wise to do so in a well-ventilated room.

Other irreversible effects caused by solvent abuse

The following damage can be caused by solvent abuse:

Central nervous system or brain damage – toluene (found in paint sprays, glues, dewaxers).

Blood oxygen depletion – organic nitrites and methylene chloride (found in varnish removers, paint thinners).

Hearing loss – this can be caused by toluene (found in paint sprays, glues, dewaxers) and trichloroethylene (found in cleaning fluids, correction fluids).

Bone-marrow damage – benzene (found in gasoline).

Peripheral neuropathies or limb spasms – this can be caused by hexane (found in glues, gasoline) and nitrous oxide (found in aerosols, gas cylinders).

Liver and kidney damage – toluene-containing substances and chlorinated hydrocarbons (found in correction fluids, dry-cleaning fluids)

① In the space below, can you list some reasons why young people decide to abuse solvents?

_____

_____

_____

_____

77

ACTIVITY

In your opinion, do people who use solvents go on to abuse other illegal drugs?

_____

_____

'The sale of solvents should be banned in Ireland.'
Discuss this statement by either agreeing or disagreeing with it and present your findings to the class group.

_____

_____

_____

_____

4. Smoking and its effects

Read the following statements and tick the boxes to indicate whether you believe the statement is true or false.

	True	False
Lung cancer is a key cause of death in Ireland.		
It is illegal to smoke in restaurants and pubs in Ireland.		
Nicotine is not addictive.		
Smoking increases the risk of heart disease by 50 per cent.		
Smoking at home can cause accidental fires.		
Breathing other people's smoke does not harm you.		
Smoking makes exercise or playing sports easier.		
Smoking contributes to premature ageing.		
Smoking causes wrinkles.		
Smoking helps you to relax.		
Smoking causes your clothes and hair to smell.		
Smoking is easy to give up.		
Smoking is ok.		

Did you know . . . ?

♦ It is believed that tobacco was first introduced to Ireland by Sir Walter Raleigh during the fifteenth century.

♦ Tobacco comes from the *Nicotiana tabacum* plant.

♦ Originally, smoking was thought to have medicinal values and was often prescribed for headaches and toothache!

♦ Today, tobacco can be legally sold to anyone over 16. However, smoking cigarettes is addictive and can seriously damage your health or cause death.

What is in a cigarette?

1. Nicotine is a poisonous substance found in all cigarettes. It is addictive, it raises blood pressure and affects the nervous system.
2. Cigarette smoke contains thousands of chemical compounds – e.g. lead, cyanide and arsenic.
3. Tobacco tar is a brown substance that coats the lungs and the trachea. Tar is absorbed by the body and contains many chemicals.
4. Carbon monoxide is a poisonous gas also found in cigarettes: this slows down the flow of oxygen into the blood.

1 If tobacco is so unhealthy for us, why is it legal?

_____

_____

_____

2 Can you name some of the diseases associated with smoking?

_____

_____

_____

3 In the space below, list some of the reasons why young people start smoking.

_____

_____

ACTIVITY

Simon is 15 years old and has been smoking for the last two years. He started smoking because his friends were smoking and he would have felt left out if he had said no the first time it was offered. Now he is playing rugby and wants to improve his fitness, but is finding it difficult to stop smoking.

What advice would you give Simon to help him stop smoking? How can Simon be assertive in this situation?

_____

_____

_____

Do you think Simon is being influenced by peer pressure to continue smoking?

_____

_____

Discuss the social and financial implications of smoking.

_____

_____

_____

_____

④ If 20 cigarettes cost €8.00 and Simon smoked 15 a day, how much money would he spend in:

A week €_____

A month €_____

A year €_____

Signpost ⤳

What you have learned in Module 8 (Influences and Decisions) will be useful to you in this module.

⑤ Can you think of other things Simon could do with this money?

_____

_____

_____

_____

_____

⑥ Find out what your school's policy is on smoking, alcohol and drug use.

School policy on:

Smoking

_____

_____

_____

_____

Alcohol

_____

_____

_____

_____

Drug use

_____

_____

_____

_____

ACTIVITY

A In groups, design a set of questions and answers for a table quiz from the information you have gathered on your school's policy on smoking, alcohol and drug use. Each group can present their questions in the table quiz. What was the most popular question asked?

_____

_____

B Were there any topics not included in the questions from the class?

_____

_____

C Pick one of the topics in this chapter and make a presentation to your class. The topic could be presented as a poem, an essay, a drawing or written work.

_____

_____

_____

_____

_____

_____

_____

MODULE 10

Personal safety

This module looks at how to ensure your personal safety. The change from primary to secondary school means more freedom for young people.

You may have noticed, though, that as this freedom and independence increase, responsibility for personal safety increases too. You also become responsible for the safety of others around you.

In this chapter we will learn about:

1 Looking after yourself

2 Safety at school

3 Road safety

4 Safe home

1. Looking after yourself

Growing up involves learning how to look after yourself by being able to recognise situations and places that may threaten your personal safety.

Practising personal safety is about understanding the need for rules and safety practices in school, at home and elsewhere, and about how following such rules reduces the risk of injury, distress or even death.

What is an accident?

First of all, we need to understand the meaning of the word 'accident'! According to the dictionary an accident is 'a misfortune or mishap causing injury' or 'an unexpected and undesirable event, especially one resulting in damage or harm'.

Accidents do happen, but by practising safety rules and responsible behaviour you can help to prevent most accidents. By understanding how an accident can happen, we can learn how to prevent it from happening again.

① Can you list three places where you think most accidents occur?

    i   _____

    ii   _____

    iii   _____

② In pairs, can you list the types of accidents that might happen in each of these places?

    i   _____

    ii   _____

    iii   _____

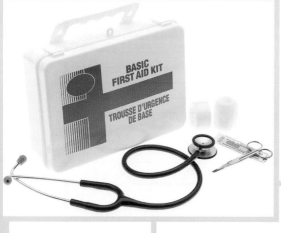

ACTIVITY

Now look at the picture below and answer these questions:

A Describe what you see in the picture.

_____

_____

_____

B What do you think is going to happen next?

_____

_____

_____

C How serious could these accidents become?

_____

_____

_____

D Who or what do you think is responsible for each accident?

_____

_____

WE CAN REDUCE ACCIDENTS BY:

- Behaving responsibly.
- Making changes to our environment.
- Taking care!

ACTIVITY

In your copybook, write out a list of the people or factors responsible for the accidents in the picture on page 84.

Then break into groups to discuss who or what has caused this accident.

Discuss the reasons for your choice with your group and nominate one person to write down all the shared points.

Nominate a speaker to represent your group and to share your group's views with the rest of the class.

2. Safety at school

You have investigated how accidents can happen and how it is the responsibility of each individual to behave safely. This personal responsibility for our own safety and others' is also carried into school. Many avoidable accidents occur in schools and that is why schools place a strong emphasis on safety procedures and responsible conduct within their codes of behaviour.

Finding out about your school's code of behaviour

1) What are the safety rules in your school?

_____

_____

_____

_____

_____

2) How does your school ensure that everybody knows these rules?

_____

_____

3) Are there some areas in your school where accidents are more likely to occur? Name these 'accident black spots'.

_____

_____

ACTIVITY

- Divide into groups for the different accident black spots in your school (see example given in the table below).
- Then write up safety rules for that area in the accident black-spot worksheet below.
- Nominate a speaker for each group to present the sets of new rules to the class for comment.
- Present these suggestions to your teacher.
- Display these safety rules in the accident black-spot areas or on the school notice board.

Accident black-spot worksheet

Location	Potential dangers	Environmental changes needed	Rules of behaviour for this location
• Woodwork room	• Personal injury with tools	• All tools to be stored in correct place after use	• Always pay attention when using tools: use them in the way you are instructed to use them • Never mess with tools or throw them around

School fire drill

④ Can you outline your school's procedure for fire drills in the space below:

_____

_____

_____

_____

⑤ Having practised your fire drill, do you feel confident that you know how to react in case of fire?

_____

_____

3.Road safety

In the table below we have listed different ways in which we may use the road. In pairs, list safety rules for each of these people:

	Person	Rules for day	Rules for night
1.	Pedestrian		
2.	Pedestrian in urban area		
3.	Pedestrian on a country road		
4.	Person getting on and off a bus		
5.	Person getting in and out of a car		
6.	Cyclist in urban area		
7.	Cyclist in rural area		

Can you outline the rules for safely crossing the road?

_____

_____

_____

_____

The National Safety Council of Ireland has had many road safety campaigns over the years, the most notable being their television advertisements.

Recall the recent road safety ad campaigns and look at the advertising strategies that are used by answering the following questions:

1. What age group do you think these advertisements are targeting and why?

_____

_____

2. What message are they trying to get across to the viewer?

_____

_____

_____

_____

3. What hazardous and risky behaviour are these advertisements highlighting?

_____

_____

_____

_____

ACTIVITY

Design a storyboard for a TV advertisement on road safety. Your ad could focus on the hazards on the road for a pedestrian, cyclist or car driver. Explain the storyline behind your advert underneath each box.

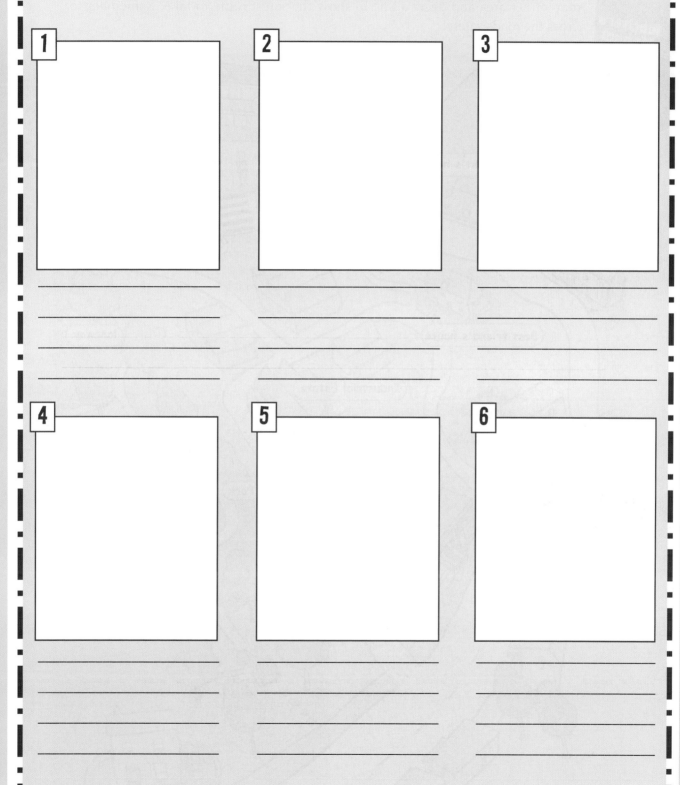

4.Safe home

Niamh walks to and from school each day by taking the safest route. Look at the map of her area and draw a line to show the safest route to take. Remember to cross the roads safely!

Teacher's Manual

Niamh's school

Her Aunt's house

Football field

Crossing

Best friend's house

laneway

Industrial Estate

Garda barracks

Park

Crossing

Shops

Shops

Niamh's home

Staying Safe

Staying safe is all about staying in control by being aware of what you are doing when you are out and also trusting your instincts. This will involve preparing for going out, looking confident, avoiding risks and never assuming it won't happen . . .

Before you go anywhere, ask yourself the following questions:

◆ Where am I going?

◆ How am I going to get there?

◆ How am I getting back?

◆ Am I prepared in case my plans change?

◆ Does someone know where I am?

When travelling

◆ Always tell someone where you are going and when you expect to return.

◆ Don't keep all your valuables in one place; carry your keys, phone and some money for the journey home in different pockets – and in pockets rather than a bag.

◆ Watch out for pickpockets. Keep your valuables secure and out of sight.

◆ Be alert when out and about and do not carry bags where you cannot see them – for example, on your back.

◆ Trust your instincts – they are there to warn you of danger.

◆ People are not always what they seem, even people you think you know.

◆ It is not weak to walk away from trouble.

When travelling on public transport

◆ Sit near other passengers and avoid isolated carriages on the bus, train, Dart or Luas.

◆ Sit on an aisle seat or near the driver where possible.

◆ Be aware of the risk of pickpockets, and when on crowded buses and trains keep your possessions close.

◆ Move away from other passengers who make you feel uncomfortable.

◆ If using a taxi, text the registration number to a friend or parent.

◆ When walking, just walk – don't listen to music, speak on the phone or send text messages because these things are distracting and prevent awareness of potential dangers.

Asking for help

It is important that if you need to look for help you go to the right people:

◆ Identify safe places along your route home or on your way to school, e.g. shops and the homes of relatives and friends.

◆ Contact a trusted adult, e.g. a garda.

◆ Text a parent or friend.

Draw a line starting from your first day at secondary school. Illustrate the events that occurred for you during each month (if possible) of your first year in your new school. Have a look at Edith's visual diary to get you started!

Edith's visual diary

me
Edith

First Day
September
(nervous)

class
teachers

met so many
new people

October
met Jenny
we became friends

January

Jenny + I joined
the basketball team
(she is brilliant at
sports)

Christmas test
I got a B in maths
(first time ever)

My maths teacher
said I showed
great ability

November
I accidentally
interrupted a
5th yr class
(v. embarrassing)

February
I had to ask
the principal for permission
to invite a guest speaker
to our school for S.P.H.E.
class. He said yes + that
I was very polite +
mannerly

my mam

March
1st yr P/T meeting.